Dear Grace—

In light of your recent baptism, we thought a book like this might be nice for you.

You have great potential! You are very bright, fun, kind, and super cute :) You have a wonderful family that loves you so much and would do anything for you.

We hope you will use prayer to help you through your life. Prayers are always answered! Sometimes the answer is yes (whoo-hoo), sometimes it's no (hmmm) and sometimes it's "not yet" (which helps you to have patience and faith). We love you very much and love watching you grow and become better each day. Merry Christmas!

Love, Grams + Gramps

THE POWER OF SARAH'S PRAYER

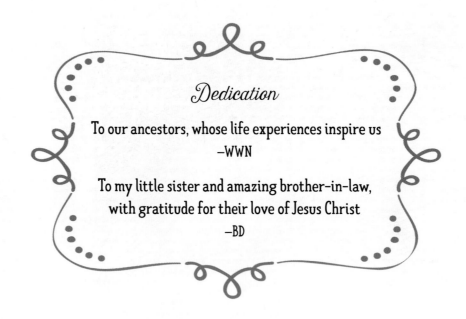

Dedication

To our ancestors, whose life experiences inspire us
—WWN

To my little sister and amazing brother-in-law,
with gratitude for their love of Jesus Christ
—BD

Library of Congress Cataloging-in-Publication Data
CIP data on file
ISBN 978-1-62972-952-7

Printed in China
RR Donnelley, Dongguan, China 5/2021

10   9   8   7   6   5   4   3   2   1

THE POWER OF SARAH'S PRAYER

Written by

WENDY W. NELSON

Illustrated by

BRANDON DORMAN

DESERET
BOOK

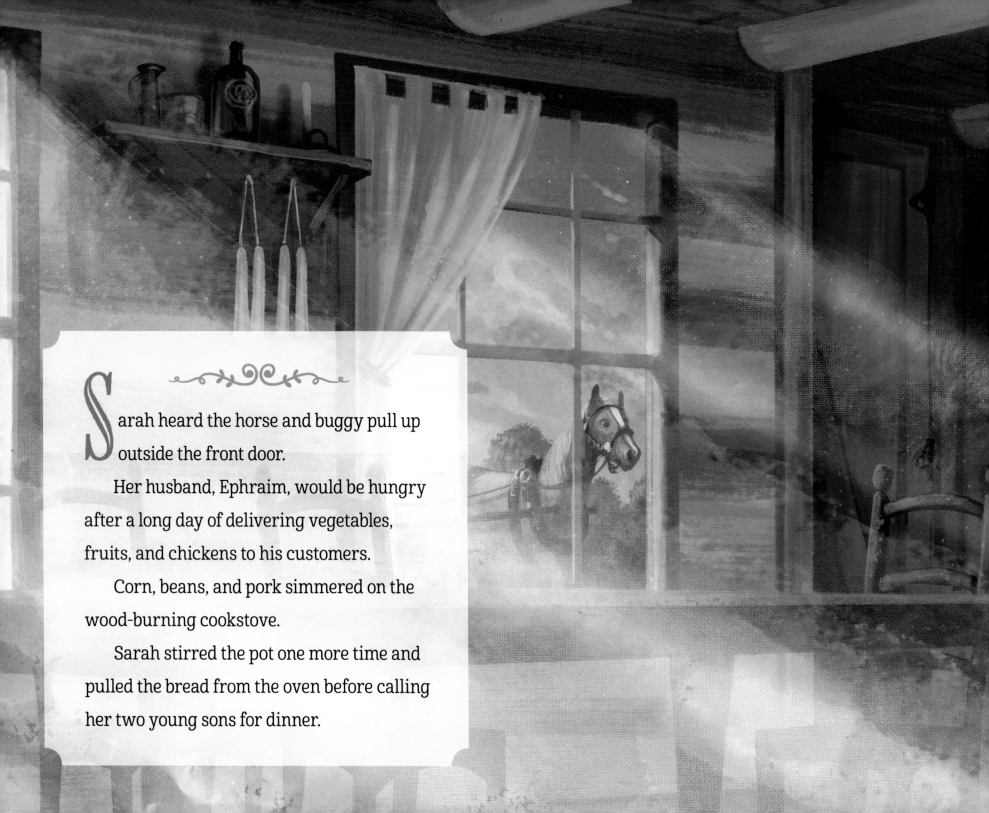

Sarah heard the horse and buggy pull up outside the front door.

Her husband, Ephraim, would be hungry after a long day of delivering vegetables, fruits, and chickens to his customers.

Corn, beans, and pork simmered on the wood-burning cookstove.

Sarah stirred the pot one more time and pulled the bread from the oven before calling her two young sons for dinner.

Sarah, I have two visitors with me," Ephraim called as he opened the door.

The news of visitors put smiles on the boys' faces.

Sarah sighed. What was Ephraim thinking? She was not prepared to have company tonight.

But she welcomed her husband with a kiss and hurried the boys to add two more plates to the table.

"These two young men are Mormon* missionaries," Ephraim said. "They're hungry, and we have plenty."

Sarah forced a smile and invited their guests to the table.

She had seen the missionaries in their little Iowa town and had heard terrible things about the Mormons and what they believed.

* In those days, the name "Mormon" was a word that people sometimes used to make fun of and bully members of The Church of Jesus Christ of Latter-day Saints. "Mormon" is actually the name of a revered prophet. The Book of Mormon is named for him because he was its compiler. Today, we call members of the Church "Latter-day Saints," not "Mormons," and, as directed by the Lord Himself (see Doctrine and Covenants 115:4), we refer to the Church by its correct name, The Church of Jesus Christ of Latter-day Saints.

As the missionaries chatted with the family, Sarah could no longer restrain herself.

"Young men, you are so intelligent and well-mannered.

"How can you possibly belong to such a notorious church as the Mormon church?" she asked bluntly.

One of the elders replied: "Mrs. Rosenberg, we would like to share our beliefs with your family.

"We have some booklets that explain some of our church's teachings.

"Would you be willing to read them? We could then return and answer your questions."

"Very well, I will read your booklets," Sarah said. At that point Sarah's face brightened.

She loved a good challenge, so she continued: "If I can convince you that what you believe is wrong, will you join *my* church?"

"Certainly, Mrs. Rosenberg," the second elder said. "And if we can convince you that *we* are right, will you join The Church of Jesus Christ of Latter-day Saints?"

Sarah laughed out loud. *How absurd!* she thought. She was sure the missionaries were wrong. Nevertheless, she extended her hand across the table to shake their hands to seal the deal.

The next day after breakfast, Sarah waved from the door as Ephraim left their home to deliver his vegetables.

She then kissed her sons as they went off to school.

Later, as she walked through the living room, she saw the booklets the missionaries had left.

Nothing on those pages has any value, she thought.

But she had agreed to read them, so, as a woman of her word, she opened one and started to read.

Much to her surprise, she could not stop.

Everything she read was so interesting.

Everything felt so right.

Minutes turned into hours as she read and read and read.

Sarah, I'm home."

Ephraim's words startled her. The truths written in the booklets had captured her mind and heart, and Sarah had completely lost track of time.

She half remembered telling the boys to go outside and play, but she had forgotten entirely about making dinner.

"Eph, you won't believe what has happened!" Sarah exclaimed. "Ever since you left this morning, I have been reading the booklets the missionaries left for us.

"My plan was to read what the Mormons believe and to prove them wrong.

"But look, they have all the Bible references right here.

"Please, come and sit down. Let me show you what I've learned."

"What about dinner?" Ephraim asked, his stomach rumbling.

"You make dinner, and I'll read to you," Sarah said.

Ephraim was not accustomed to making dinner, but there was something about the way Sarah looked and sounded that made it easy for him to say, "All right."

Is Father going to cook every night?" grumbled the older son. "My soup tastes like weeds."

"I found a piece of johnnycake that isn't burned!" delighted the younger son.

The next night, Sarah read some more, and Ephraim cooked again.

The more that Sarah read, and the more that Ephraim cooked, the more they talked and thought about what they were learning.

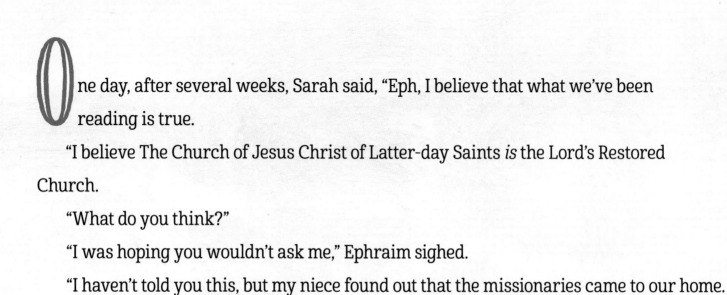

One day, after several weeks, Sarah said, "Eph, I believe that what we've been reading is true.

"I believe The Church of Jesus Christ of Latter-day Saints *is* the Lord's Restored Church.

"What do you think?"

"I was hoping you wouldn't ask me," Ephraim sighed.

"I haven't told you this, but my niece found out that the missionaries came to our home.

"She's been telling me all kinds of negative things about the Mormons.

"She said that if I join the Mormon church, people in town will not buy my produce anymore, and I'll lose my business.

"I didn't tell you because I didn't want to upset you."

Sarah thought for a moment before responding.

"I understand, dear.

"But please tell me the truth: just between the two of us, have you felt in your heart and mind that what we've been reading is true?"

Ephraim nodded, a tear rolling down his cheek.

"Yes, but I *won't* join the Mormons. I *can't,* Sarah.

"I love you and always want you to be happy, but if I lose my business, I won't be able to support you and the boys. I'm sorry."

"It's okay, Eph, you've made your decision," Sarah said. "Now, I'll make mine."

Taking a deep breath, she continued:

"I'm going to be baptized. I want to be a member of The Church of Jesus Christ of Latter-day Saints."

arah soon learned that she needed her husband's consent to be baptized. She couldn't imagine that Ephraim would give it.

And she was right.

Ephraim was determined to do everything in his power to protect his family from those who hated the Mormons.

Sarah prayed that Ephraim's heart would change.

But *nothing* changed.

In fact, when Sarah started reading the Book of Mormon, *things got worse!*

In a desperate effort to stop Sarah from thinking more about the Church and about baptism, Ephraim secretly took Sarah's precious book and burned it!

Sarah knew what her husband had done.

So, the next morning, Sarah bought another copy of the Book of Mormon and continued to read.

Then Ephraim burned *that* book!

And so it went: Sarah buying copies of the Book of Mormon and Ephraim burning them.

Finally, one day, Sarah said to Ephraim, "For every copy of the Book of Mormon you burn, I will buy another."

Her declaration stopped him in his tracks.

Ephraim knew that Sarah was a woman who said what she meant and meant what she said.

From that moment on, Ephraim did not burn one more copy.

However, Ephraim continued to refuse to give his permission for Sarah to be baptized. And Sarah continued to pray.

She prayed and she prayed *and* she prayed.

And still *nothing changed!*

Could Heavenly Father really hear her prayers?

Sarah wondered if the heavens were made of brass!

Then, one hot night in June, Sarah prayed a different prayer.

She pleaded with God:

"**Please remove every obstacle** so that I can be baptized a member of The Church of Jesus Christ of Latter-day Saints."

That very night, in the middle of the night, Sarah was awakened from a deep sleep by her two sons.

"Mother, are you all right? Come quickly!" quaked her older son.

"We have Father downstairs.

"We think he's been poisoned. Father is dying!"

As Sarah rushed down the stairs, she could hear Ephraim's anguished cries.

How had she not heard her husband's deafening moans and groans?

The slightest sound always woke her up.

Hurrying to her husband's side, Sarah remembered how she had prayed:

"Please remove every obstacle so that I can be baptized."

"Oh, no!" she blurted out. **"Not like that!"**

In the very *moment* that Sarah spoke those words, Ephraim testified that every pain in his body left.

Later, after the household had quieted, Ephraim and Sarah sat together.

He gently placed his hand over hers and asked, "Sarah, were you praying for me to die so that you could join the Mormon church?"

"No, I wasn't praying that you would *die*," she said, "but I *was* praying that **every obstacle would be removed** so that I could be baptized."

Ephraim squeezed her hand. "Well, Sarah, you may join the Mormon church."

Then he added, **"Just don't pray like that anymore!"**

He smiled and kissed her.

"And one more thing, Sarah."

His words were both tender and firm.

"You must tell *no one* that you are a Mormon."

Sarah agreed.

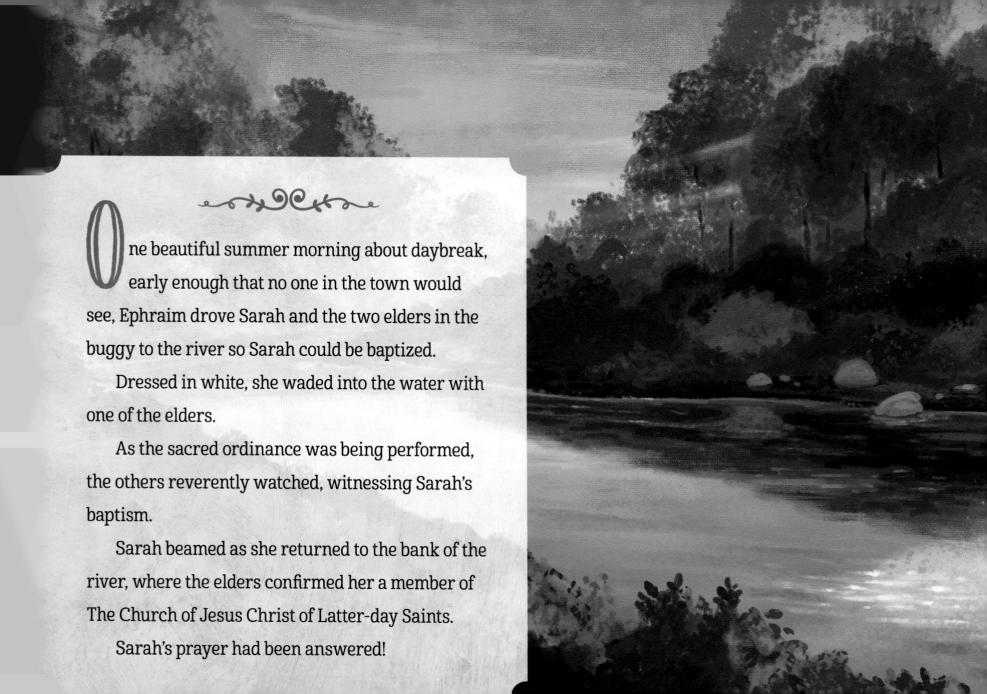

One beautiful summer morning about daybreak, early enough that no one in the town would see, Ephraim drove Sarah and the two elders in the buggy to the river so Sarah could be baptized.

Dressed in white, she waded into the water with one of the elders.

As the sacred ordinance was being performed, the others reverently watched, witnessing Sarah's baptism.

Sarah beamed as she returned to the bank of the river, where the elders confirmed her a member of The Church of Jesus Christ of Latter-day Saints.

Sarah's prayer had been answered!

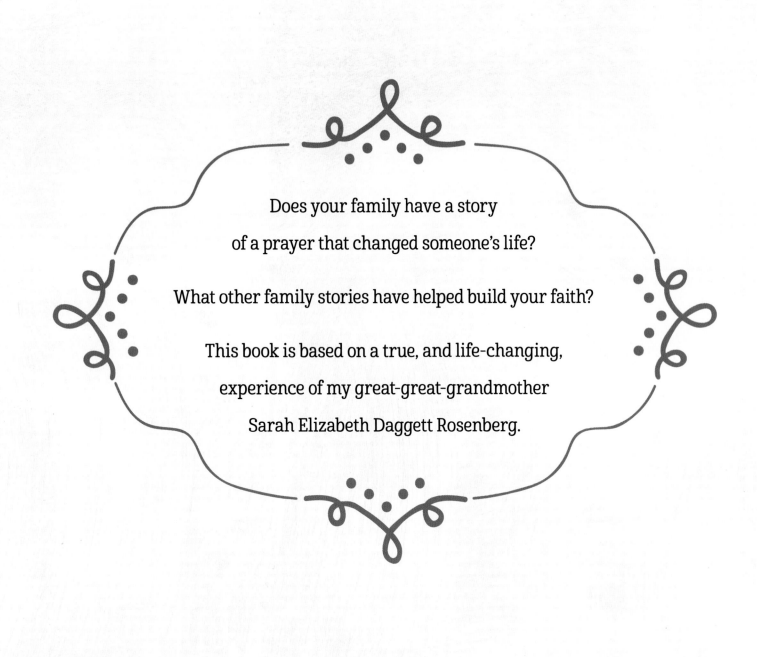

Does your family have a story
of a prayer that changed someone's life?

What other family stories have helped build your faith?

This book is based on a true, and life-changing,
experience of my great-great-grandmother
Sarah Elizabeth Daggett Rosenberg.